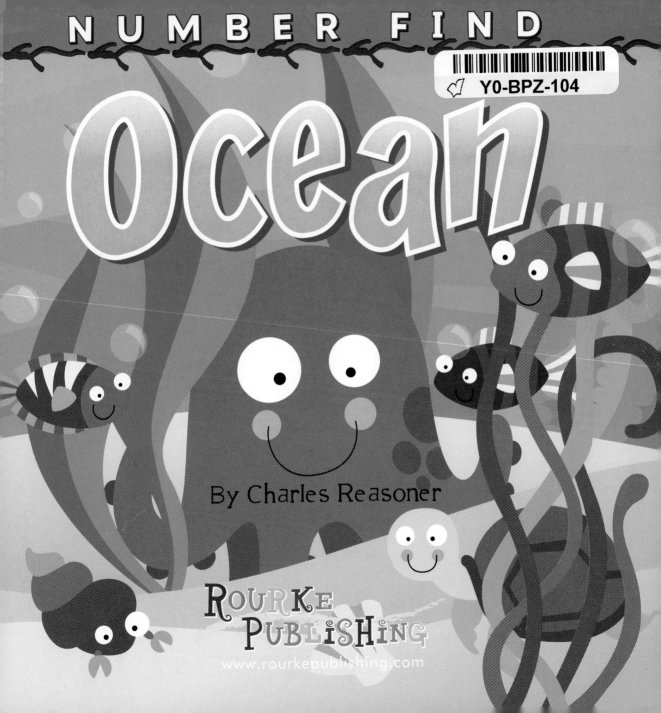

NUMBER FIND

Ocean

By Charles Reasoner

ROURKE
PUBLISHING
www.rourkepublishing.com

www.rourkepublishing.com

Cover amd Page Illustrations by Ed Myer

Art Direction and Page Layout by Teri Intzegian

Rourke Publishing
Printed in Singapore, International Press Softcom Limited
061311
061311LP

ROURKE
PUBLISHING

www.rourkepublishing.com - rourke@rourkepublishing.com
Post Office Box 643328 Vero Beach, Florida 32964

How many animals can you find?

Way out at sea and under the ocean,
Live all kinds of fish with
all kinds of motion!

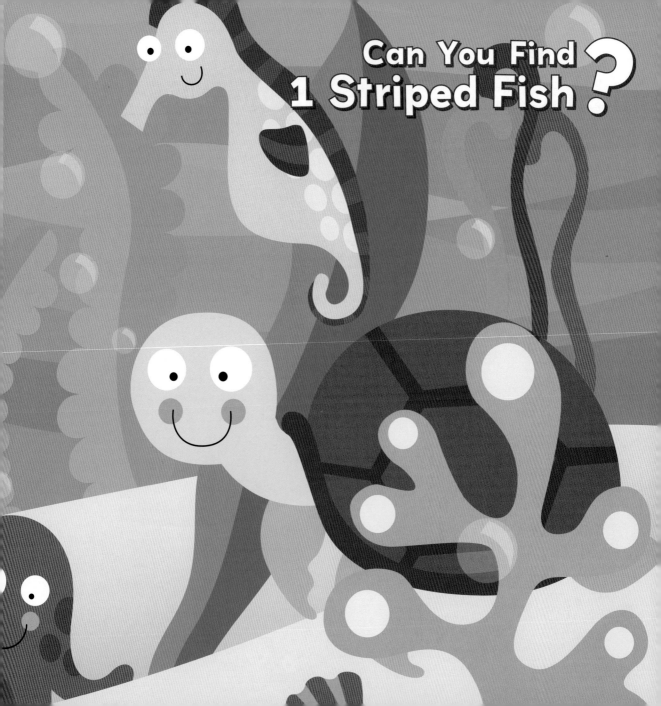

Can You Find
1 Striped Fish?

The biggest of all these things with tails,
purple one and blue one must be whales!

Can You Find
2 Whales ?

I see a crab, a seal,
and some fish that are kind,

But the starfish are
a little harder to find!

Can You Find
3 Starfish?

A shark and a lobster
and some pretty striped fish,

Sea turtles and some jellyfish!

Can You Find 4 Sea Turtles?